MARK CATESBY'S
Nature
Colouring Book

ROYAL
COLLECTION
TRUST

MARK CATESBY'S
Nature
Colouring Book

Drawings *from*
THE ROYAL COLLECTION

ARCTURUS

The Royal Collection is among the largest and most
important art collections in the world, and one of
the last great European royal collections to remain
intact. Royal Collection Trust, a department of the
Royal Household, is responsible for the care of the
Royal Collection and manages the public opening of
the official residences of the Queen. Income generated
from admissions and from associated commercial
activities contributes directly to The Royal Collection
Trust, a registered charity. Explore the Royal
Collection at www.rct.uk.

Note: Catesby's English names, as published in the
Natural History, are used wherever possible; where
Catesby does not provide an English name, his Latin
synonym is given in italics.

This edition published in 2020 by Arcturus Publishing Limited
26/27 Bickels Yard, 151–153 Bermondsey Street,
London SE1 3HA

Copyright © Arcturus Holdings Limited

All images Royal Collection Trust / © Queen Elizabeth II 2020

All rights reserved. No part of this publication may be reproduced,
stored in a retrieval system, or transmitted, in any form or by any means,
electronic, mechanical, photocopying, recording or otherwise, without
prior written permission in accordance with the provisions of the
Copyright Act 1956 (as amended). Any person or persons who do any
unauthorised act in relation to this publication may be liable to criminal
prosecution and civil claims for damages.

ISBN: 978-1-83857-573-1
CH006722NT
Supplier 29, Date 0420, Print run 10403

Printed in China

Created for children 10+

INTRODUCTION

In 1747 the English naturalist Mark Catesby (1682–1749) completed the book that had become his life's work: *The Natural History of Carolina, Florida and the Bahama Islands*. This was the first comprehensive survey of the flora and fauna of south-eastern North America, comprising 220 beautifully etched plates of birds, plants, fish, mammals, crustacea and insects, all with accompanying descriptions.

The book reflected the avid curiosity about the botanical products of the New World that was widespread at the time. Catesby's own interest in botanical specimens, particularly trees and shrubs, was not only for their intrinsic properties, but also for their practical uses in medicine, agriculture and the building industry. He also undertook an intensive study of the region's birds, which 'excelled in the Beauty of their Colours', and its fishes, which surprised him by how 'lavishly Nature had adorn'd them with Marks and Colours most admirable'.

With help and financial backing from, amongst others, the founder of the British Museum Sir Hans Sloane and celebrated botanist William Sherard, Catesby went on two extended expeditions to the then little-explored region: to Virginia in 1712–19 and to Carolina and Florida in 1722–26. Inspired by the 1707 publication of Sloane's *A Voyage to the Islands Madera, Barbados, Nieves, St Christopher and Jamaica*, Catesby also travelled to the West Indies, visiting Jamaica in 1714 and the Bahama Islands in 1725.

During these trips he painted from life the plants and animals he encountered. Believing that 'artistic' techniques of shading and perspective compromised the objective truth of his studies for the 'Purpose of Natural History', Catesby used instead what he termed a 'flat, tho' exact manner' to make a precise visual record of each specimen. The watercolours he produced acted as a basis for the etched plates of *The Natural History*. Rather than having his watercolours etched by a professional printmaker, Catesby learned to etch himself. This gave him complete control over the translation of his original watercolours into printed illustrations, thus ensuring the greatest possible degree of accuracy.

The Natural History was issued in ten parts and an appendix between 1729 and 1747, each part being presented to the Royal Society on publication. Catesby died in 1749, only two years after the project was completed. His 263 original watercolours, a selection of which can be seen here, were kept by his widow until her death in 1753. They were bought by George III in 1768 and remain in the Royal Collection to this day.

KEY: LIST OF PLATES

1 *Lilium augustifolium, flore rubro singulari*

6 Blue jay and bay-leaved smilax

3 The Ilathera Duck

4 The Parrot-Fish

5 The Large Lark

6 Prickly Apple with Zebra Swallowtail Butterfly

7 The Fox-coloured Thrush and the Cluster'd Black Cherry

8 The Summer Red-Bird and the Western Plane-Tree

9 The Flamingo

10 *Frutex rubo similis* and *Pittoniae similis*

11 The Rice-Bird and Rice

12 The Yellow-throated warbler, the Pine-warbler and the red maple

13 *Lilium, sire martagon canadense*

14 The Larger Red-crested Wood-pecker and the Live Oak

15 *Acacia foliis ampliovi-bus, siliquis cincinatis*

16 The Hooded Titmouse and the Water-Tupelo

17 *Plumeria flore roseo odoratissimo*

18 The White-crown'd Pigeon and the Cocoa Plum

19 The painted bunting, indigo bunting and sweet bay

20 The Humming-Bird and the Trumpet-Flower

21 The Wood duck

22 The Pitch Apple

23 The Tufted titmouse, pinxter flower, J. Torr and yellow star-grass

24 The Bead Snake and the Virginian Potato

25 The Mock-Bird and the Dogwood Tree

26 The Pork Fish

27 The Red-bellied Wood-pecker, the Hairy Wood-pecker and the Black Oak

28 The Yellow Titmouse and the Red Bay

29 The Blue grosbeak and sweet bay

30 The Red Bird, the Hiccory Tree and the Pignut

31 Water frog and purple pitcher plant

32 *Caryophyllus spurius inodonus Folio subrotundo scabro, Flore racemoso bexapetaloide couineo speciosissimo* and *Convulvulus minor Pentaphyllos, flore purpureo minore*

33 The Purple Gross-beak and the Poison Wood

34 The Blueish Green Snake and *Frutex baccifer*

35 The Bahama Sparrow and the Plum Cat

36 The Bahama Finch and the Broad Leafed Guaiacum with blue flowers

37 *Philadelphus flore albo majore indoro*, The Four Eye'd Night Butterfly and *Smilax norispinosa baccis rubris*

38 White frangipanni and smooth passion flower

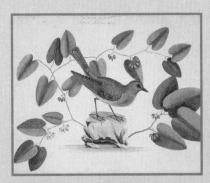

39 The Eastern bluebird and carrion flower

40 The Baltimore Bird and the Tulip Tree

41 A Monarch Butterfly, with Orchids

42 The Scarlet ibis

43 The largest Carolina moth and *Anona maxima*

The names used here are taken from *The Natural History of Carolina, Florida and the Bahama Islands*.

Smilax laevis, Salicis folio non serrato, baccis nigris

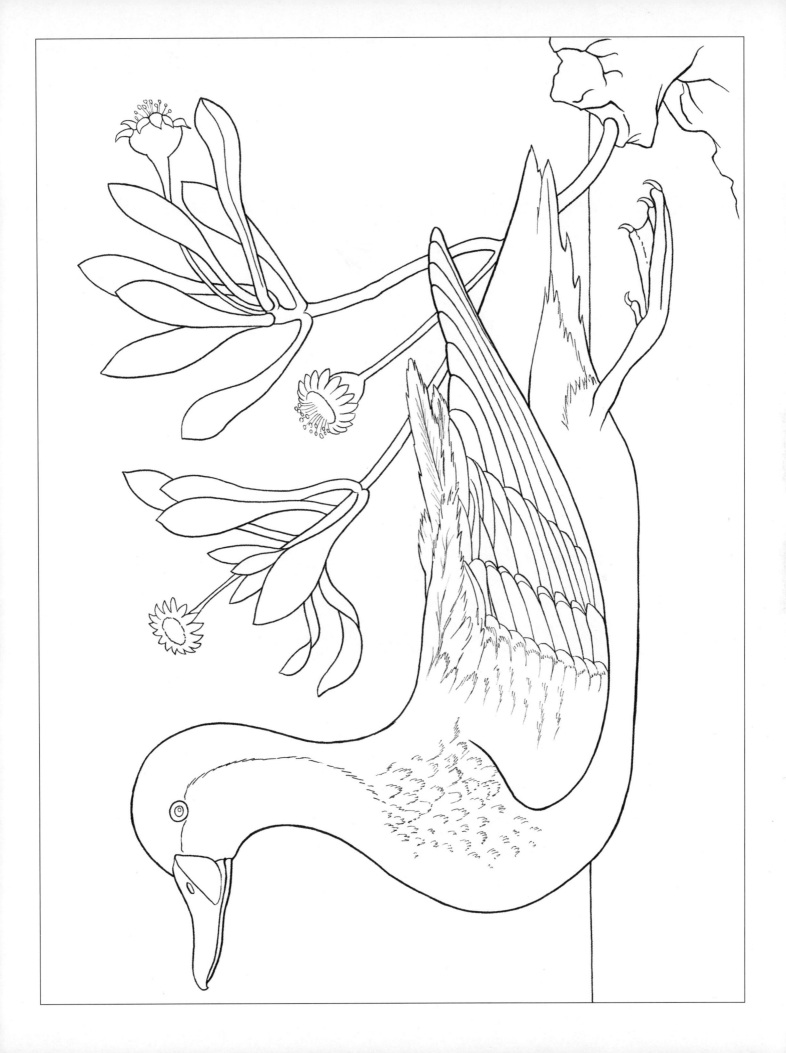

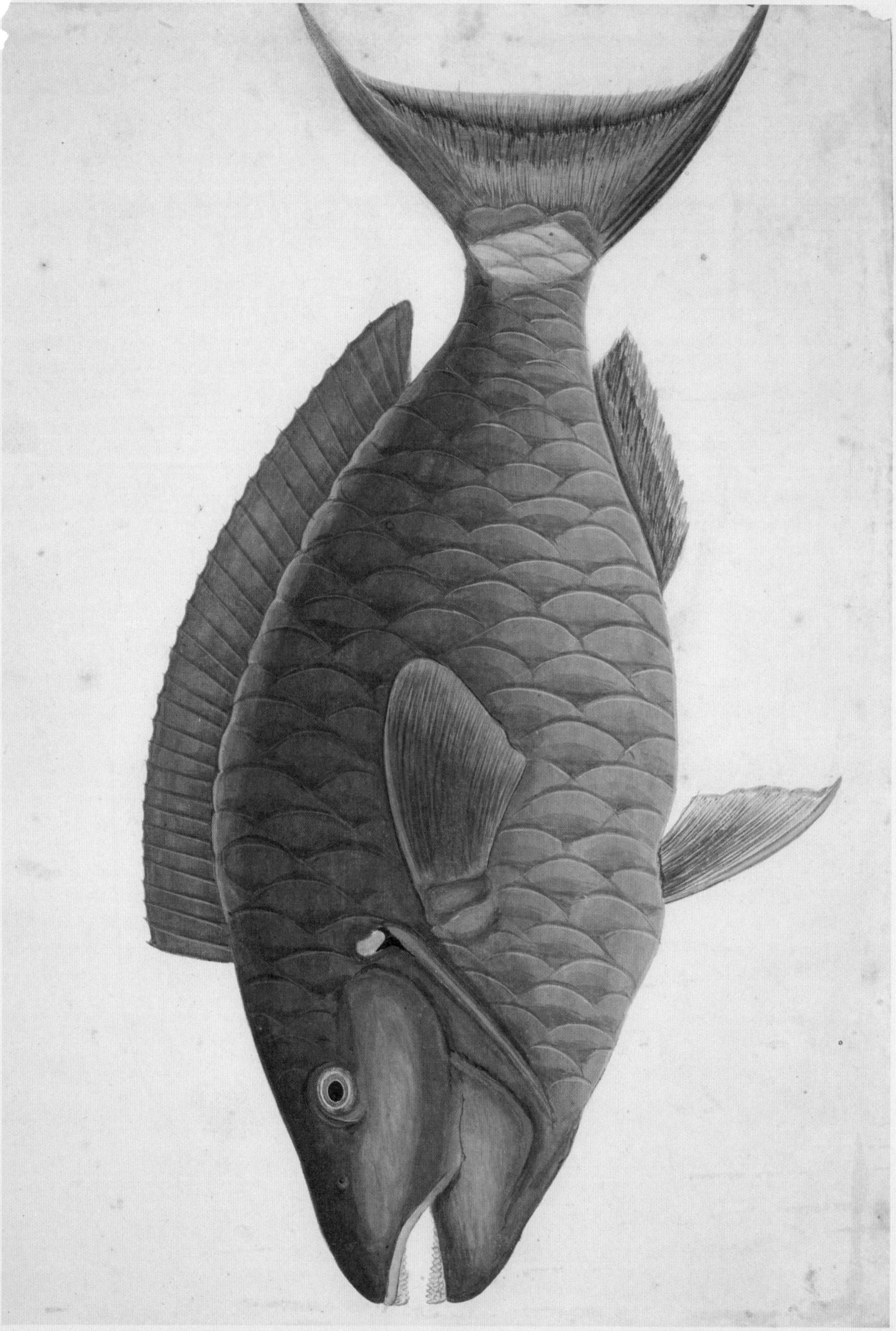

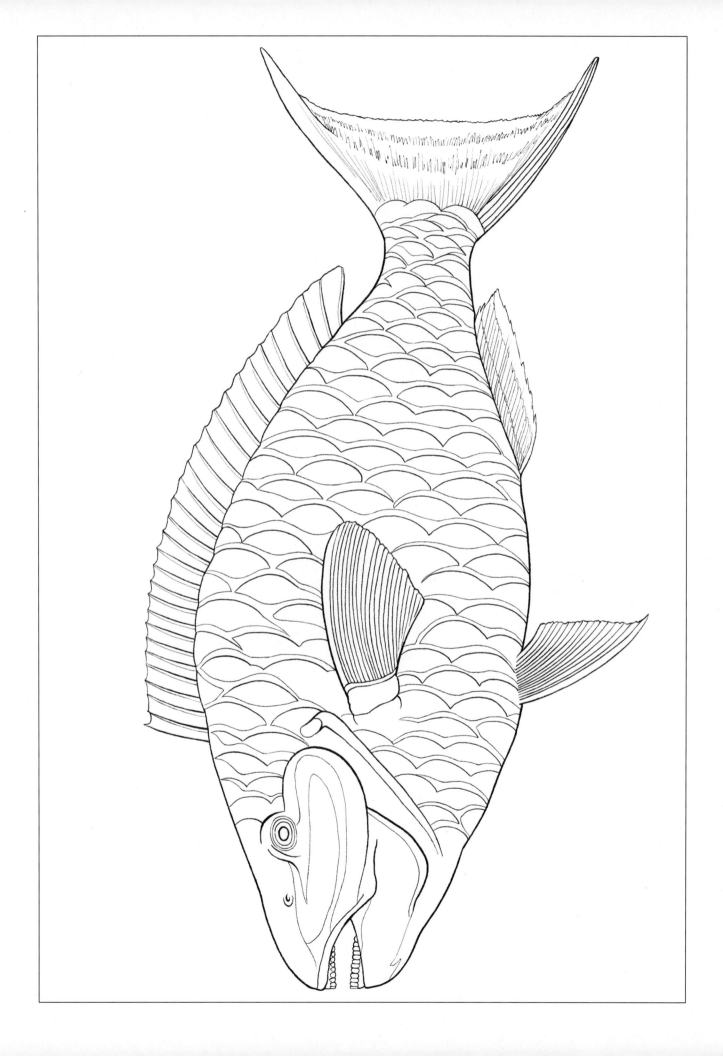

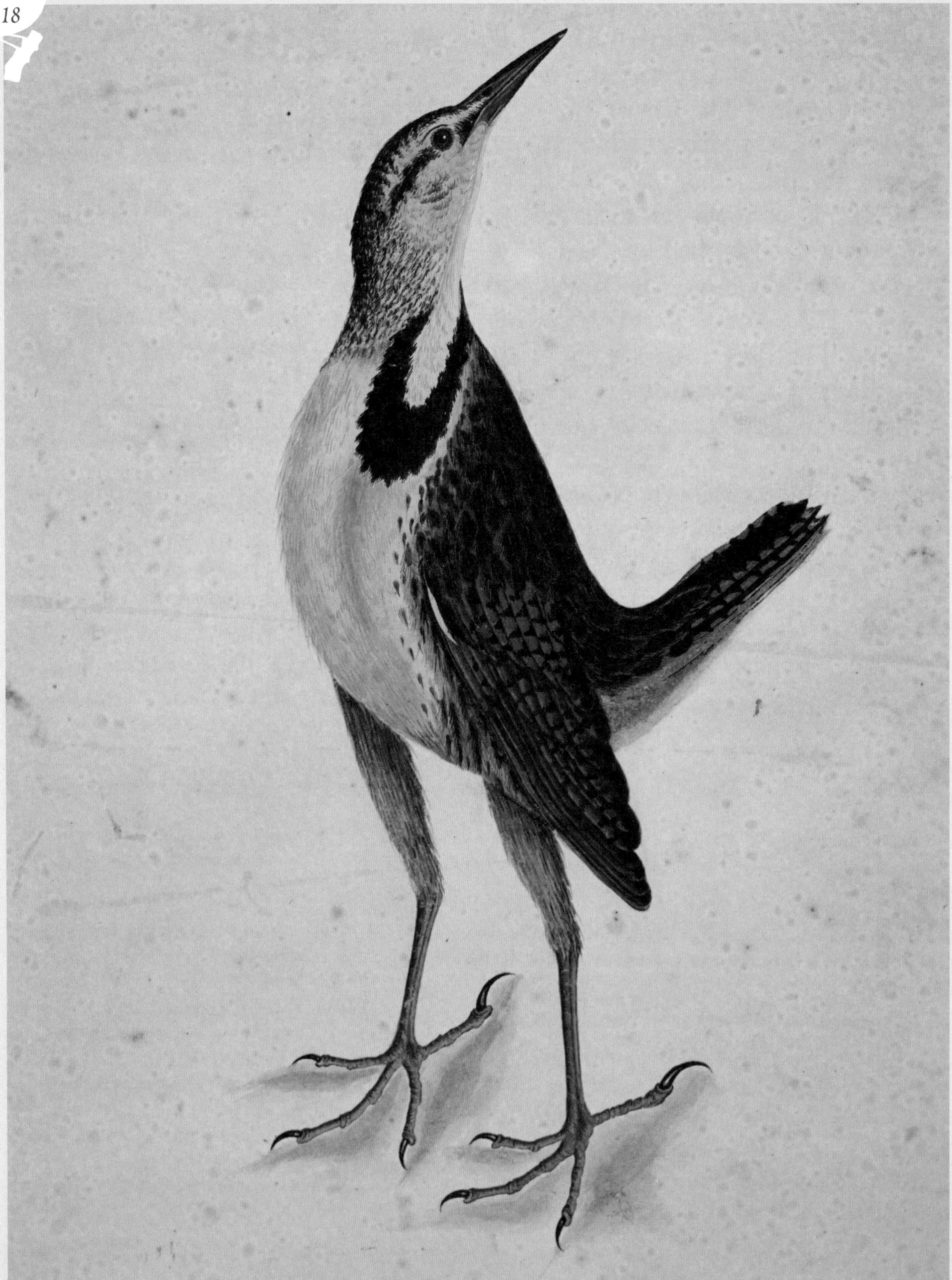

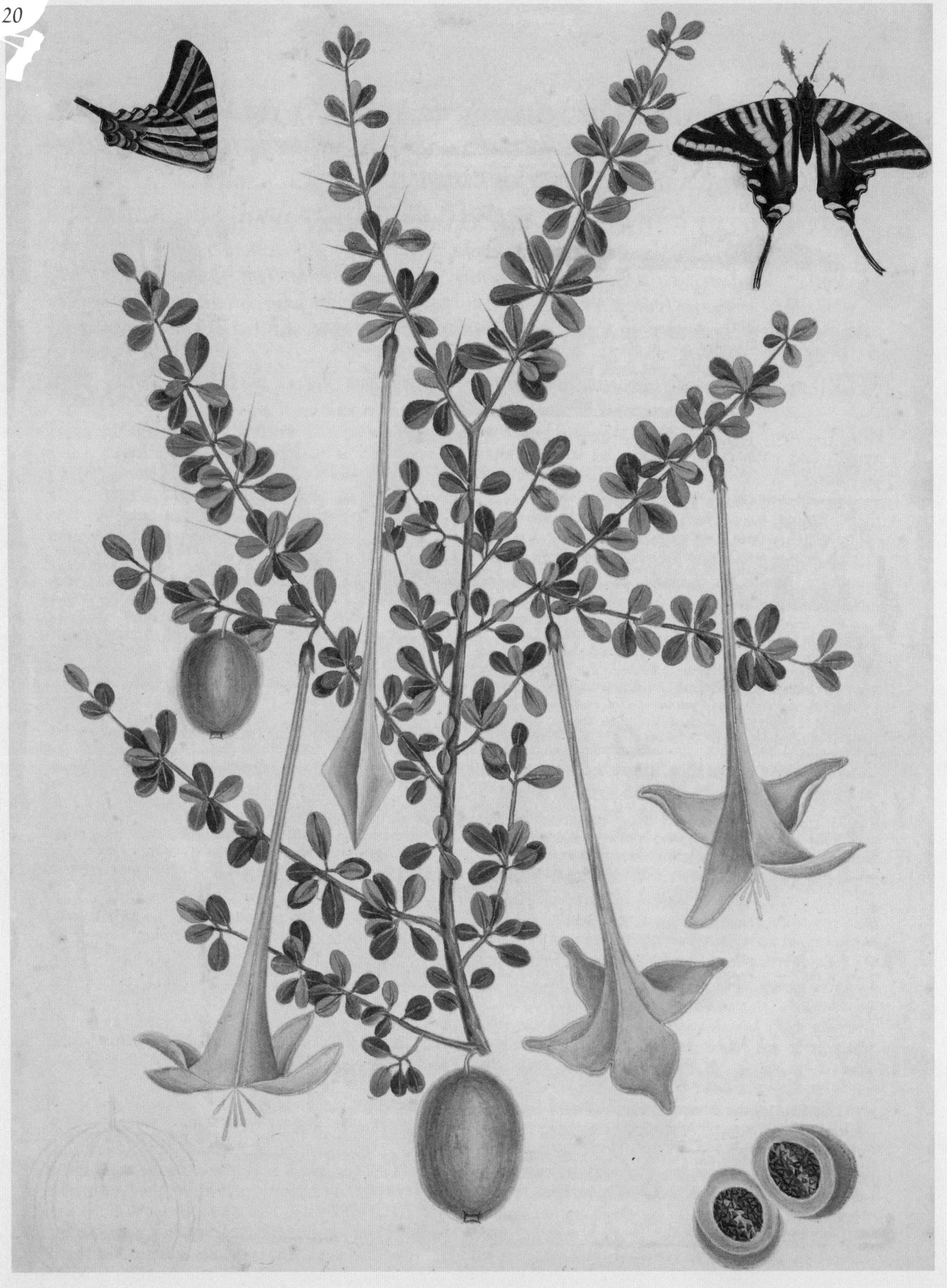

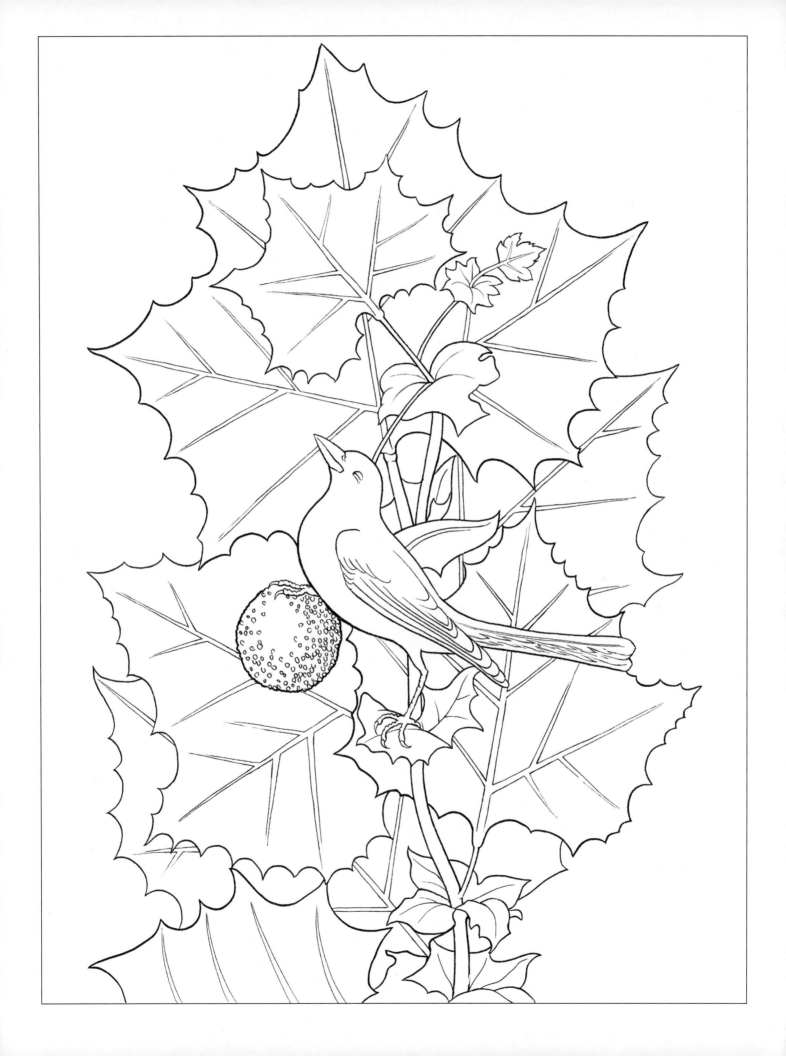

Flamingo. Phaenicopterus Bahamensis

Keratophyton dichoton fuscum

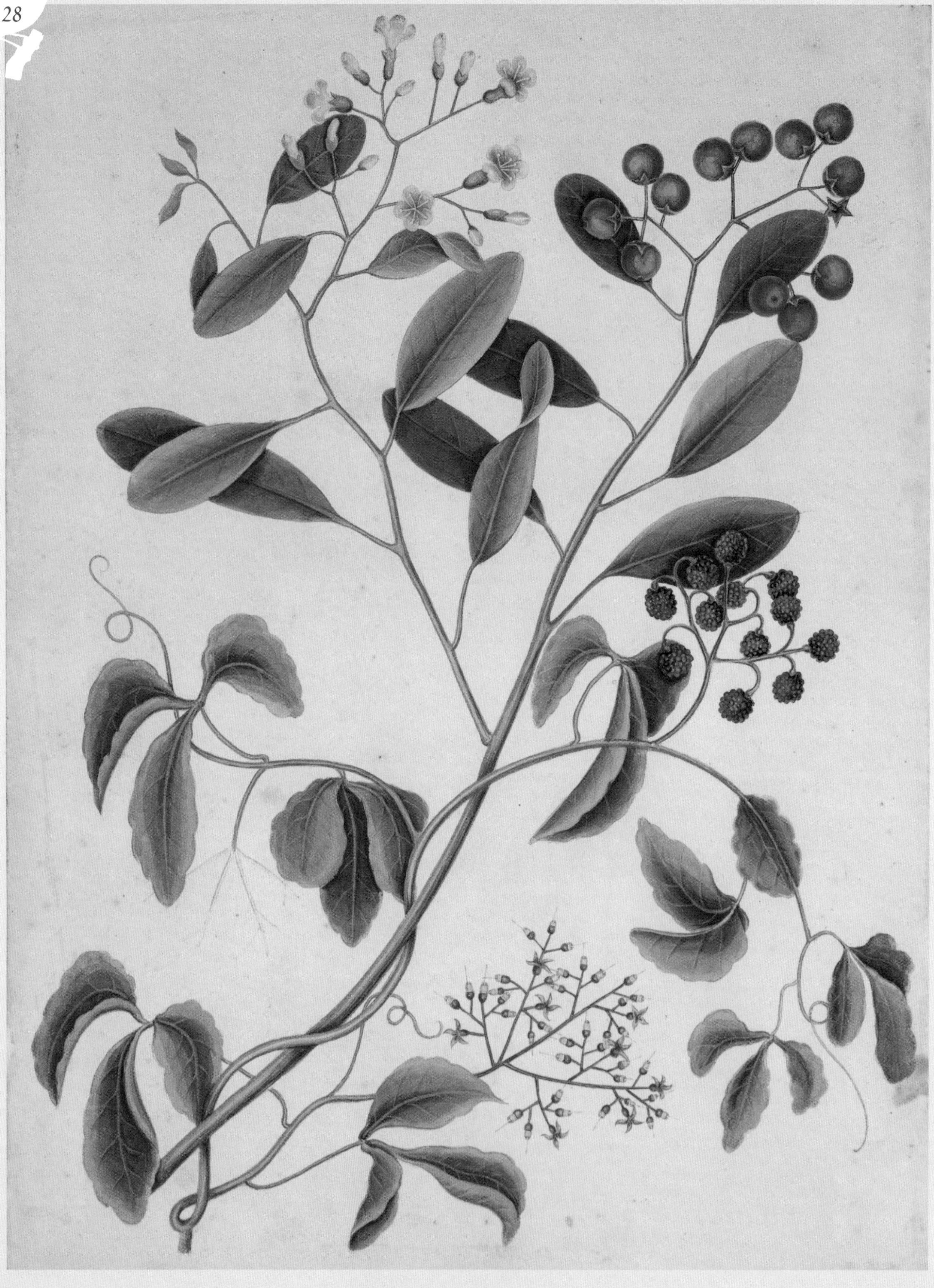

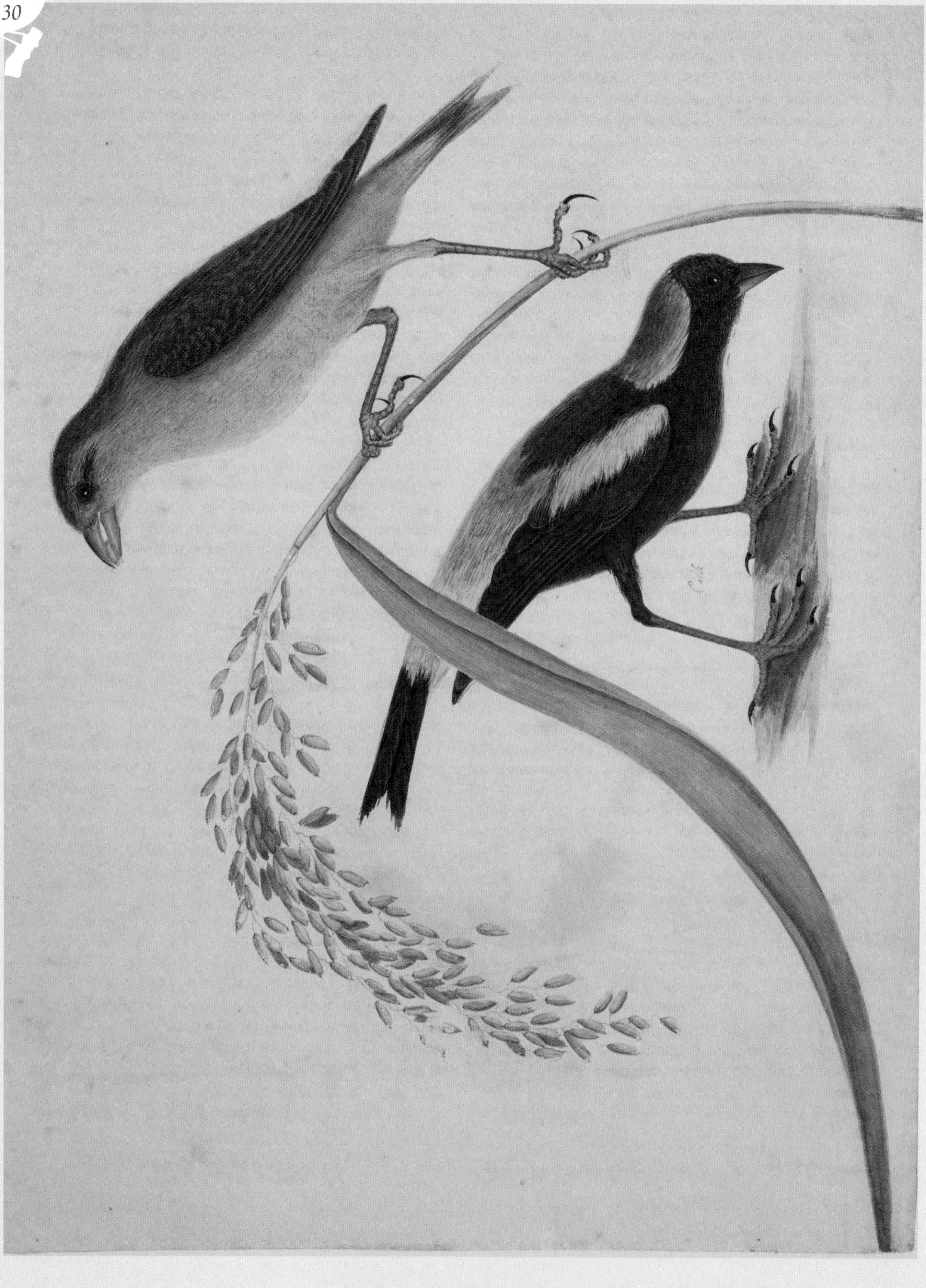

Parus Americanus cinereus

Parus Americanus cinereus

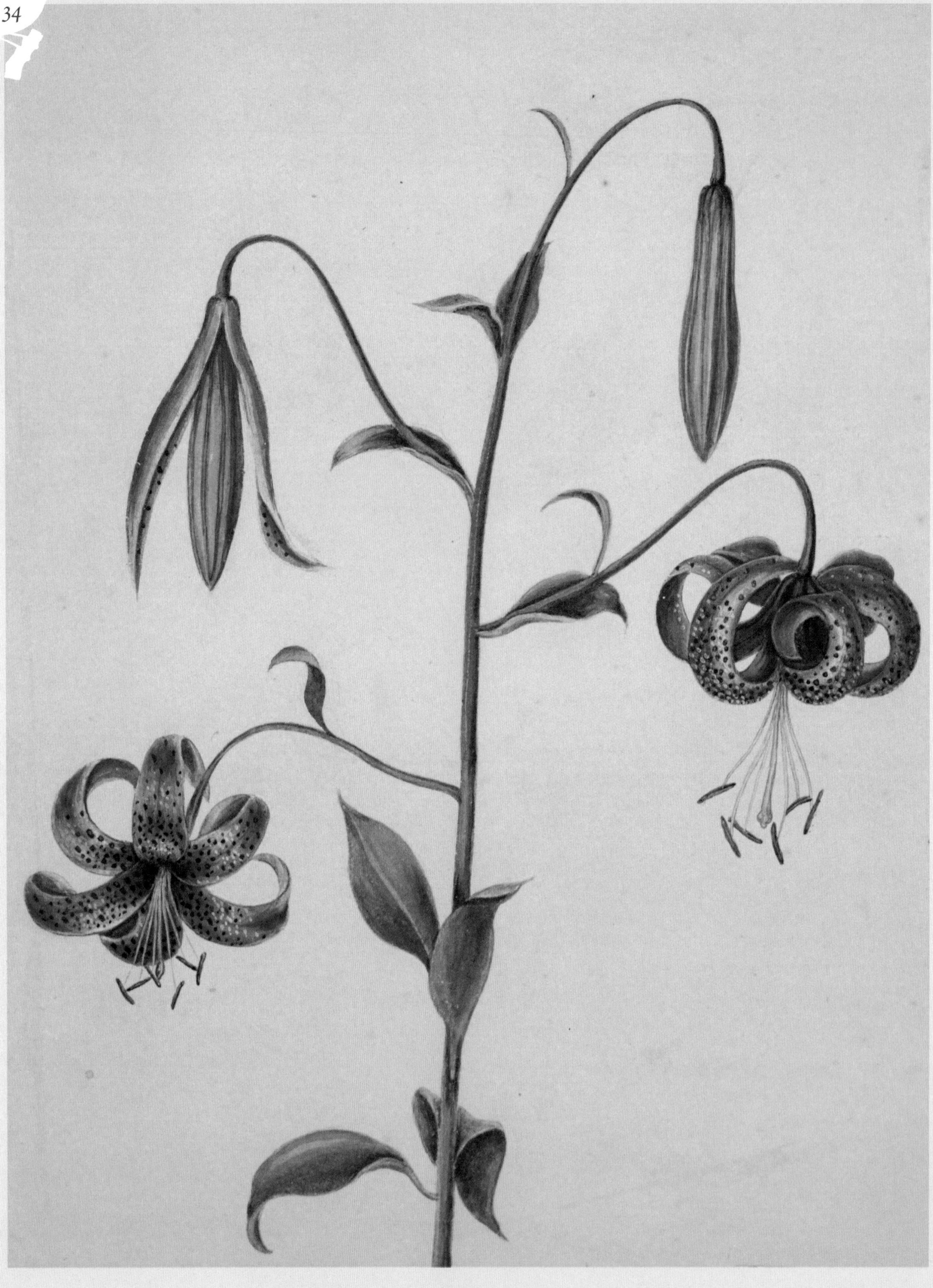

14

Acacia folijs amplioribus siliquis circinatis plum. Cat.

Arbor in aqua Nascens, folijs latis Accuminatis & dentatis fructu elæagni majore Cork Tree or Water Tupelo

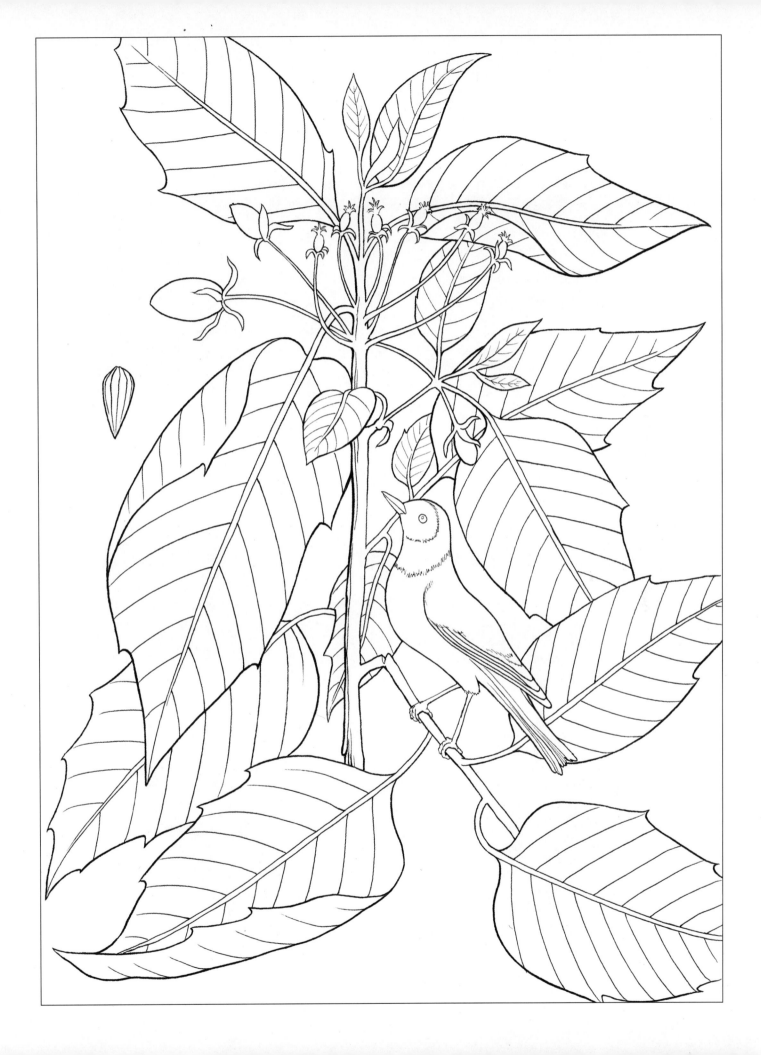

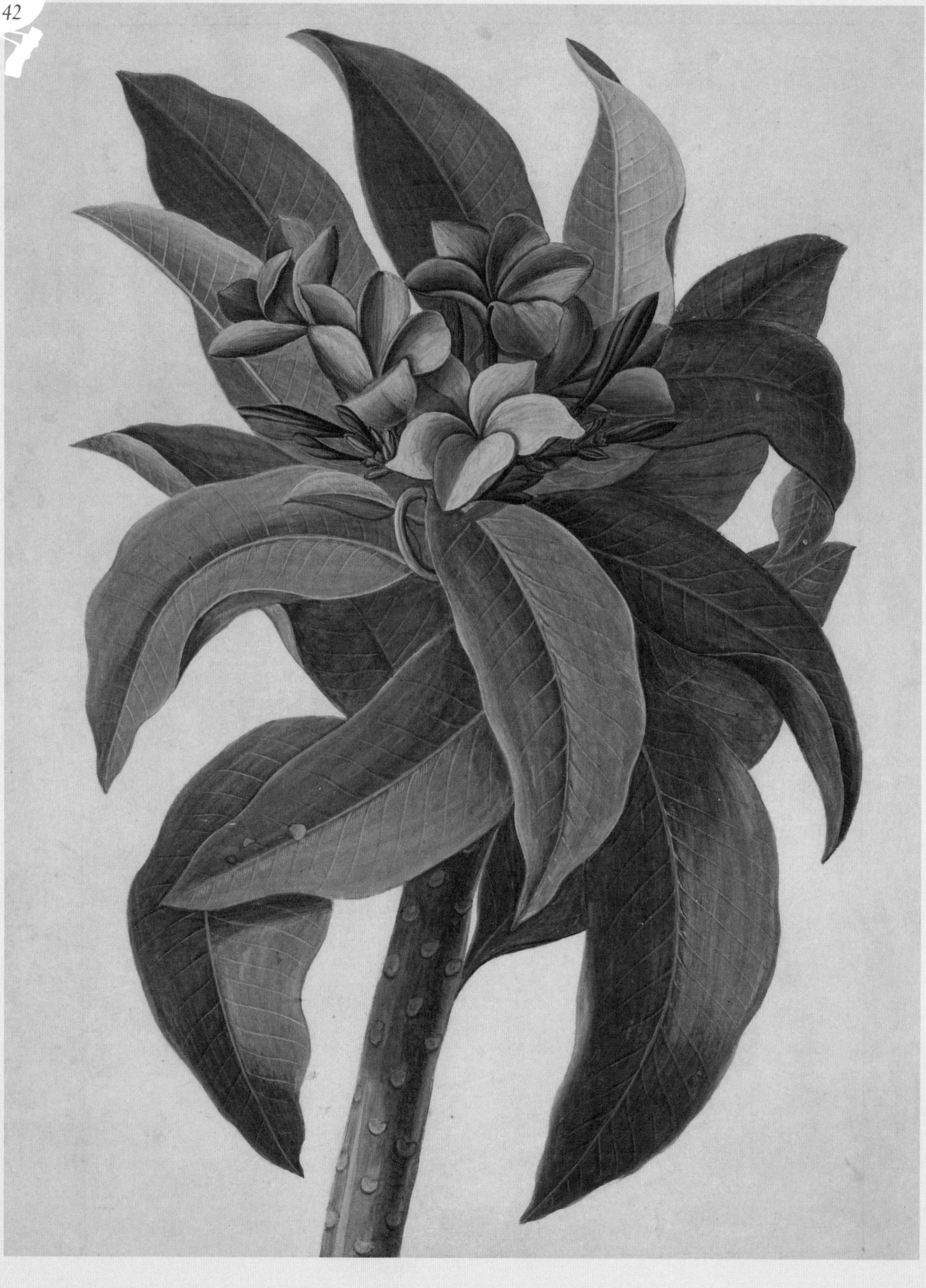

Columba capite albo

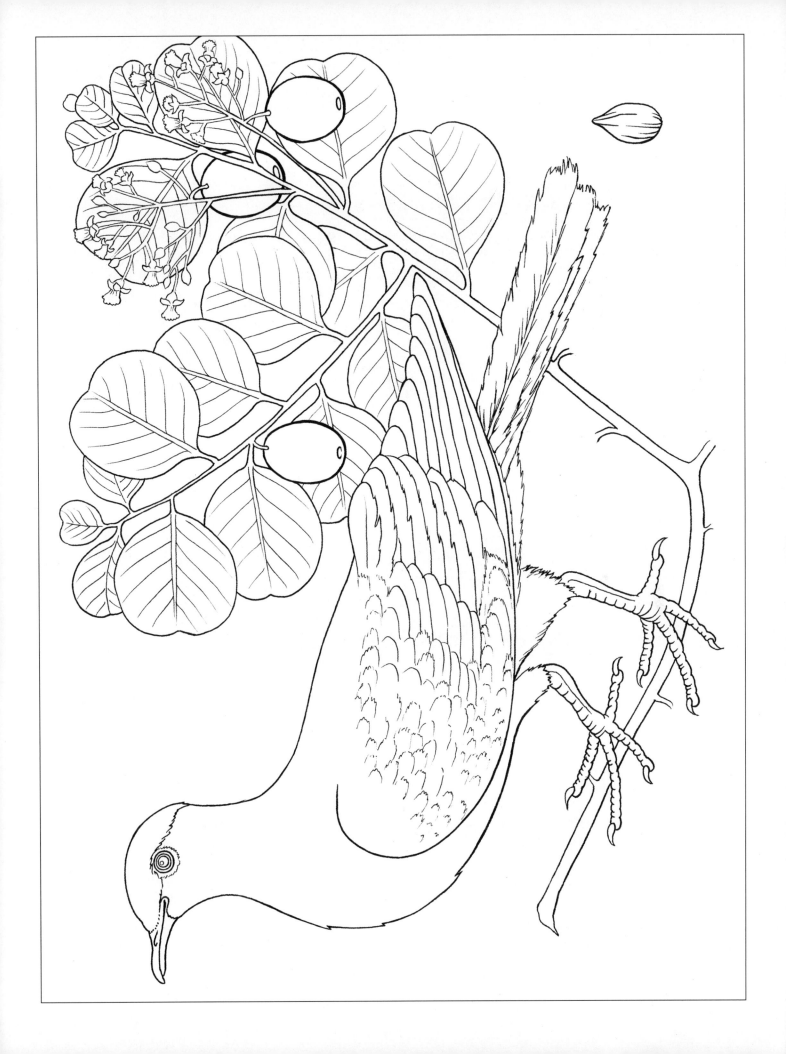

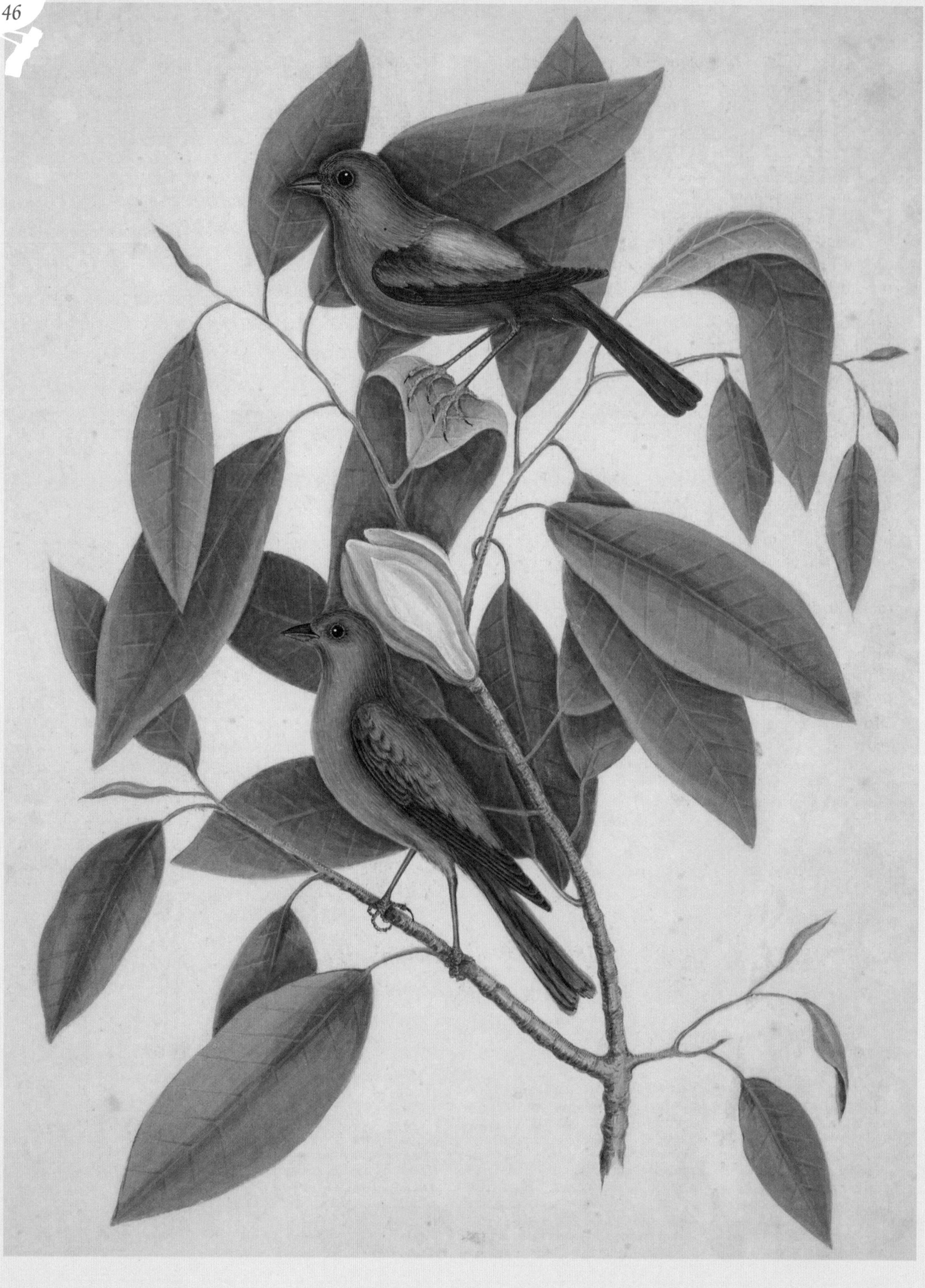

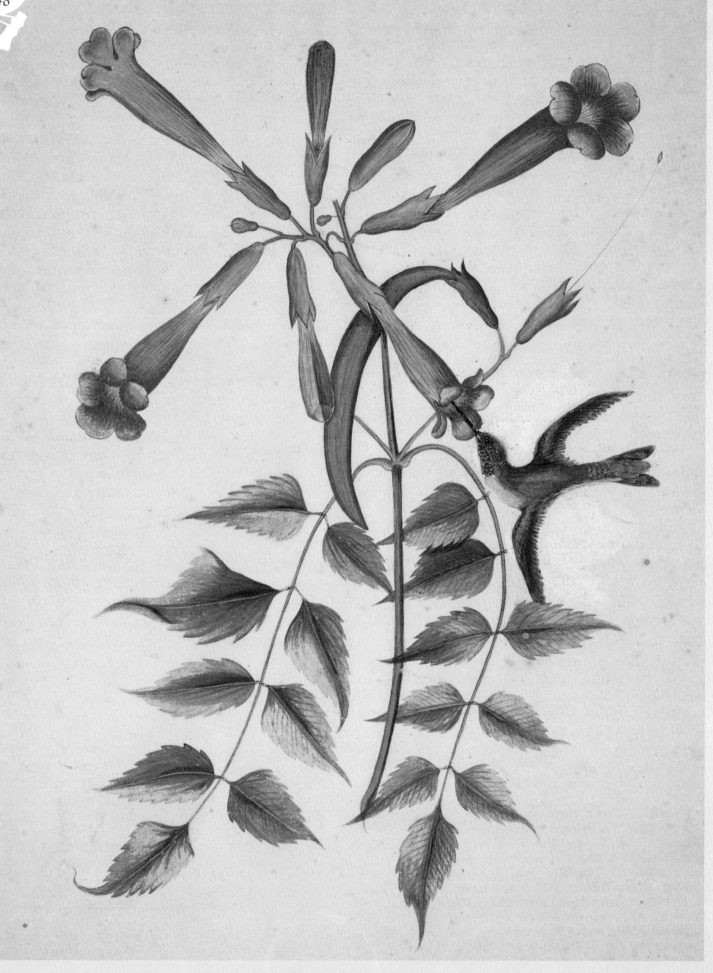

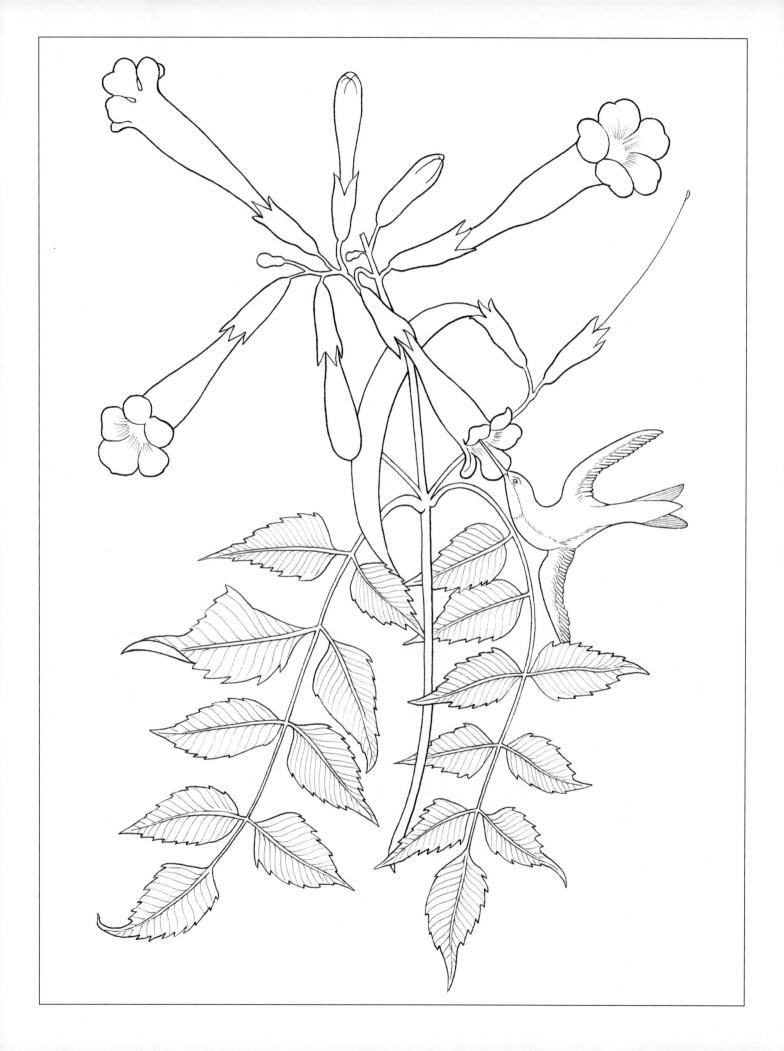

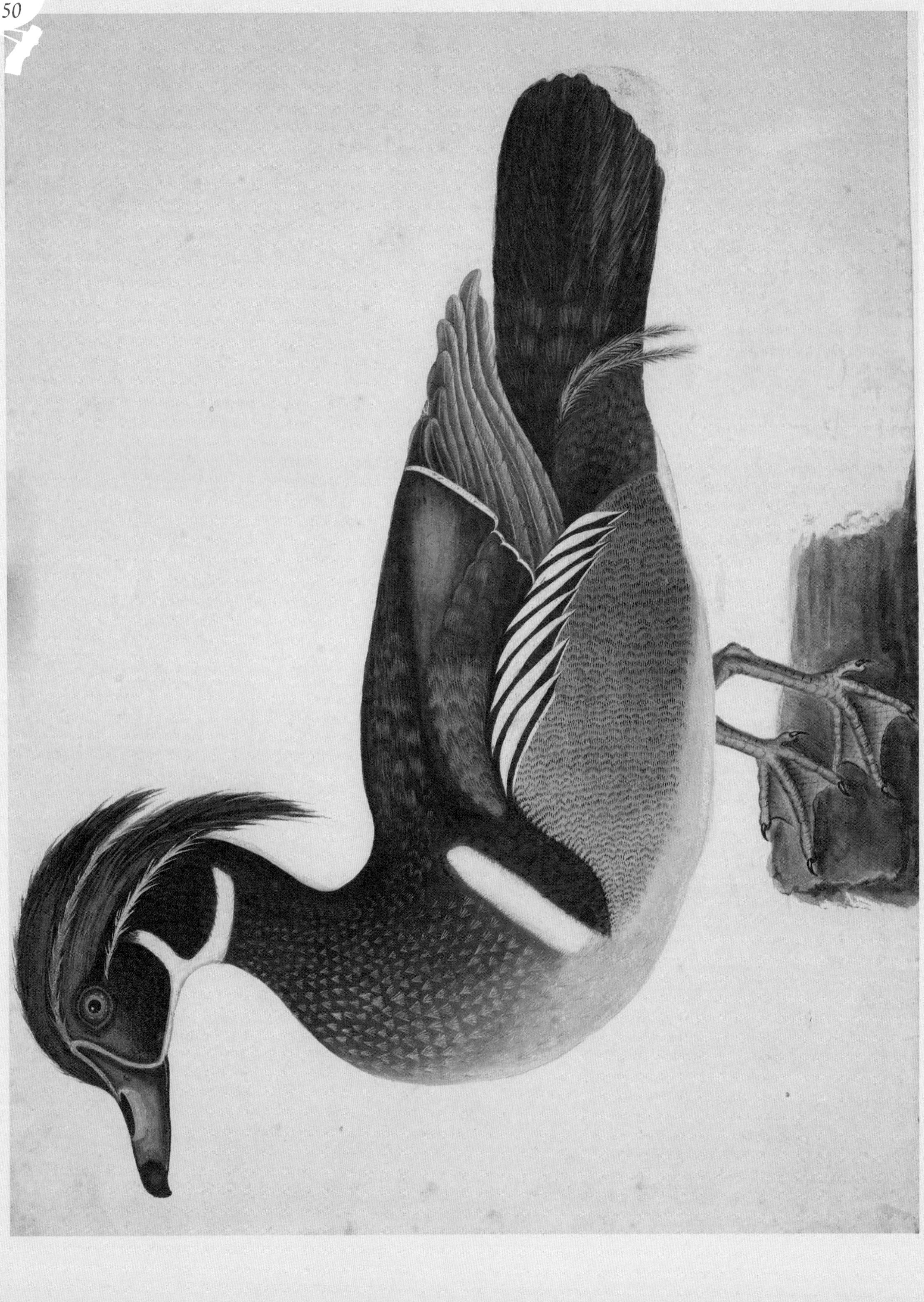

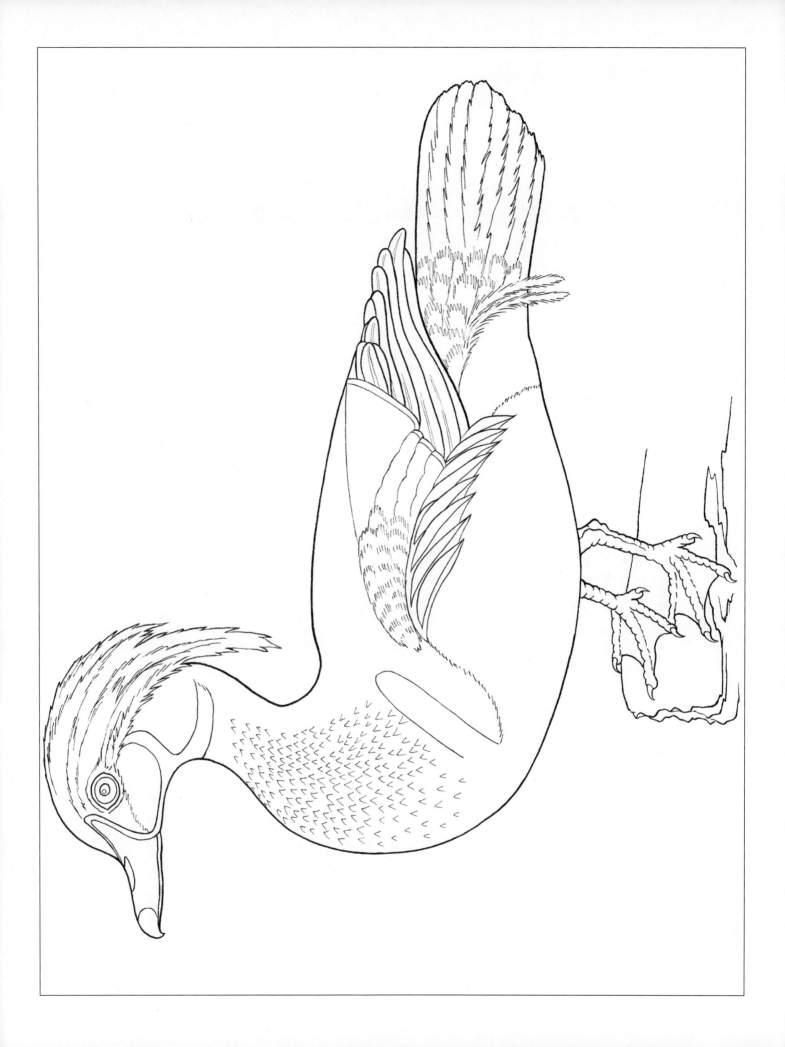

Cistus Virginiana flore & odore
periclymeni — Dom: Banister

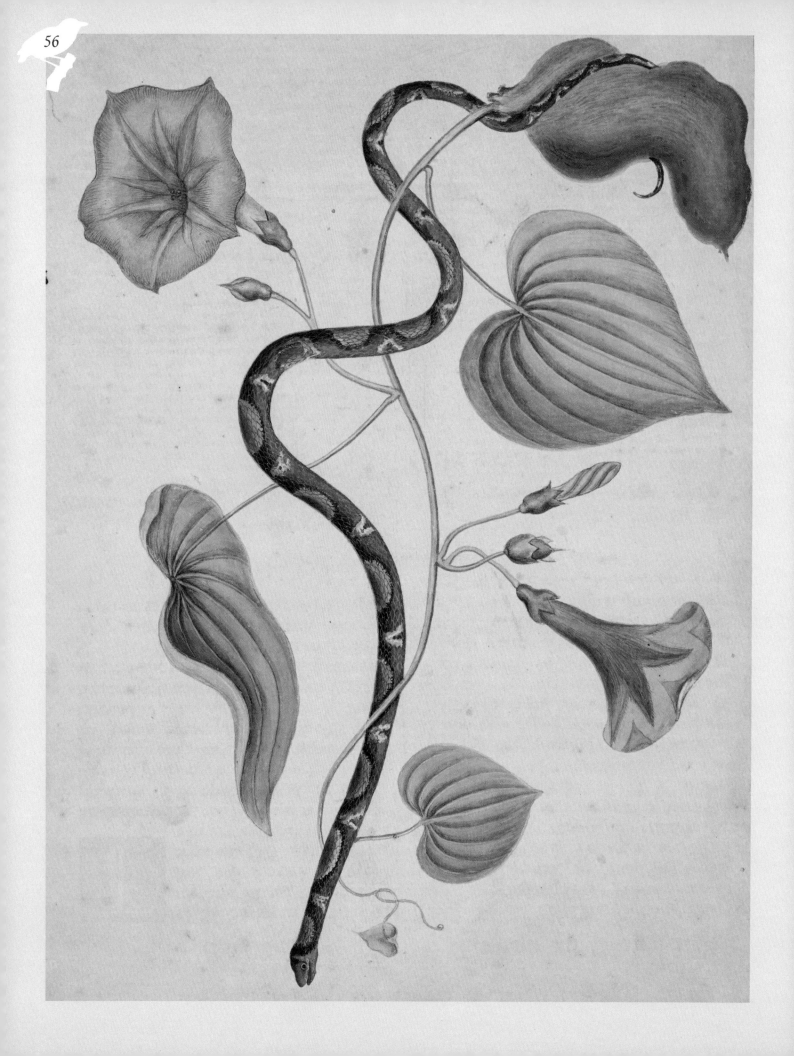

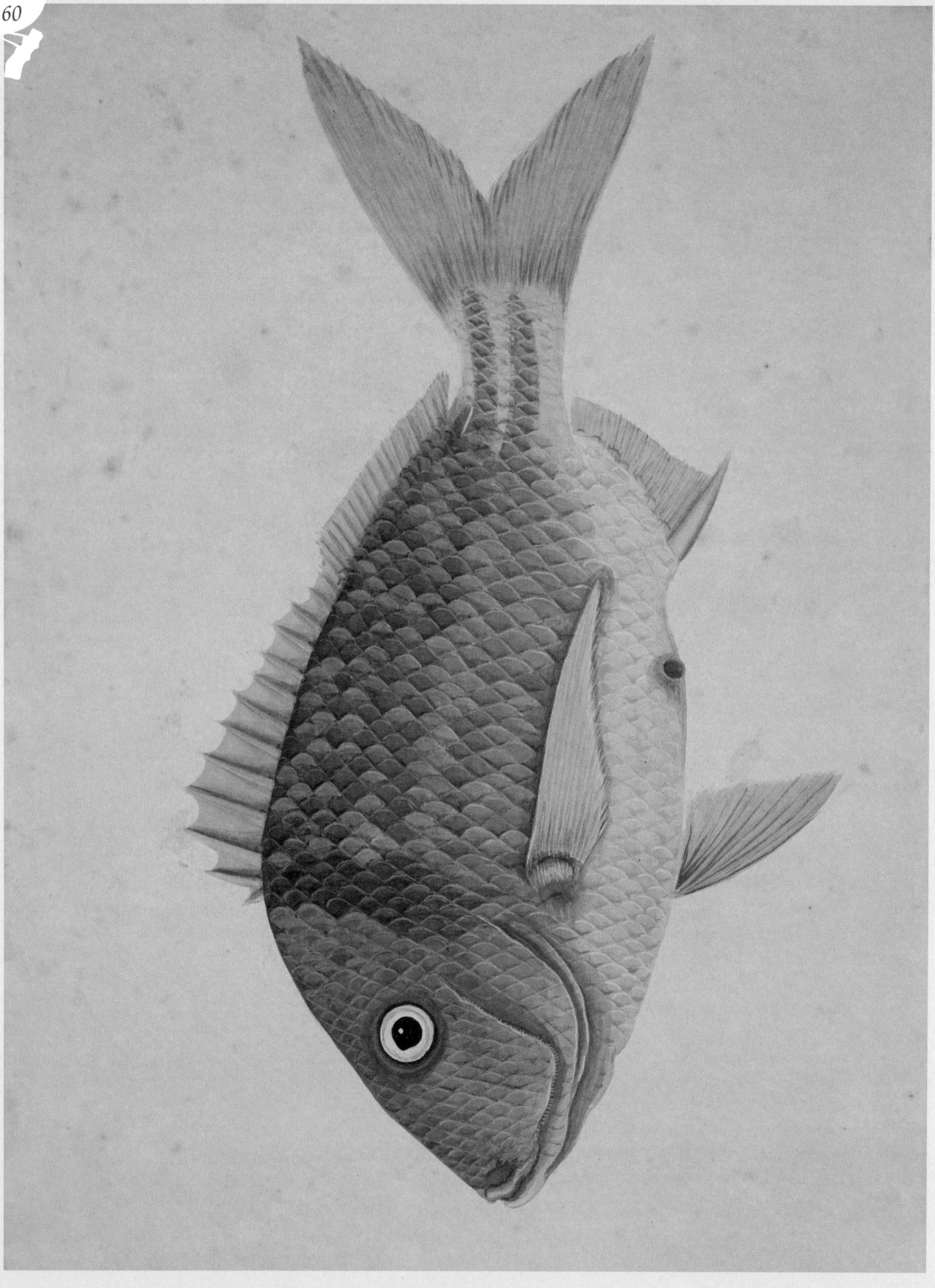

Quercus (forte) Marilandica folio trifido ac Sassafras acefens. Ray Hist: Black Oak.

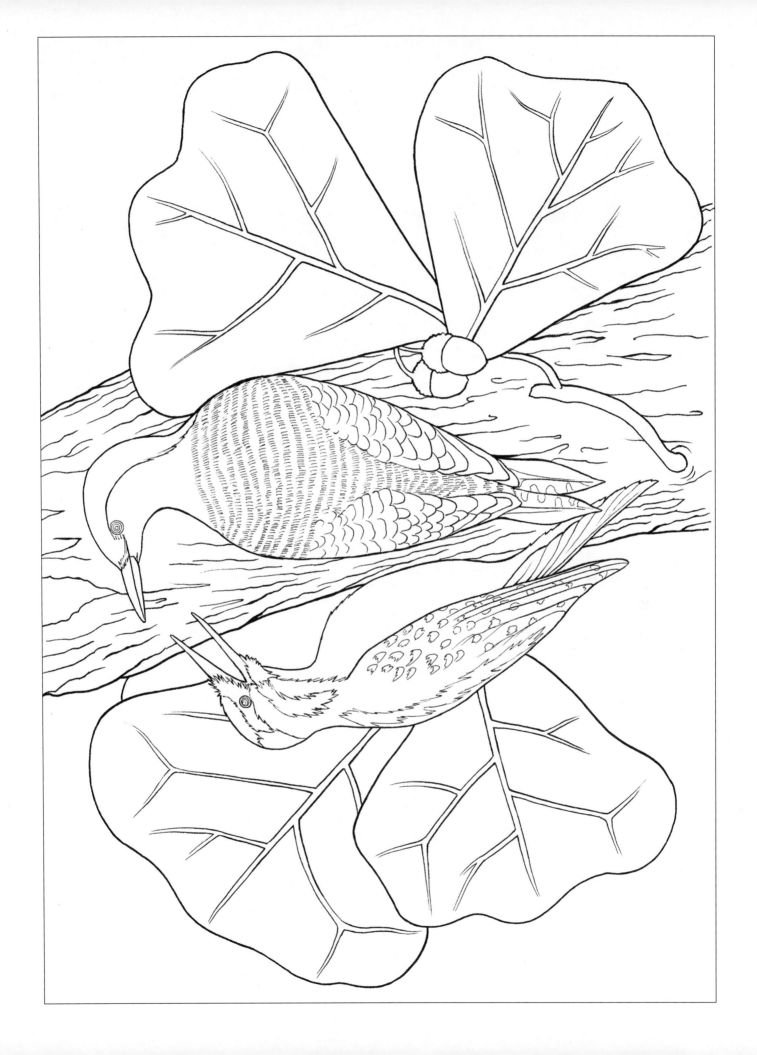

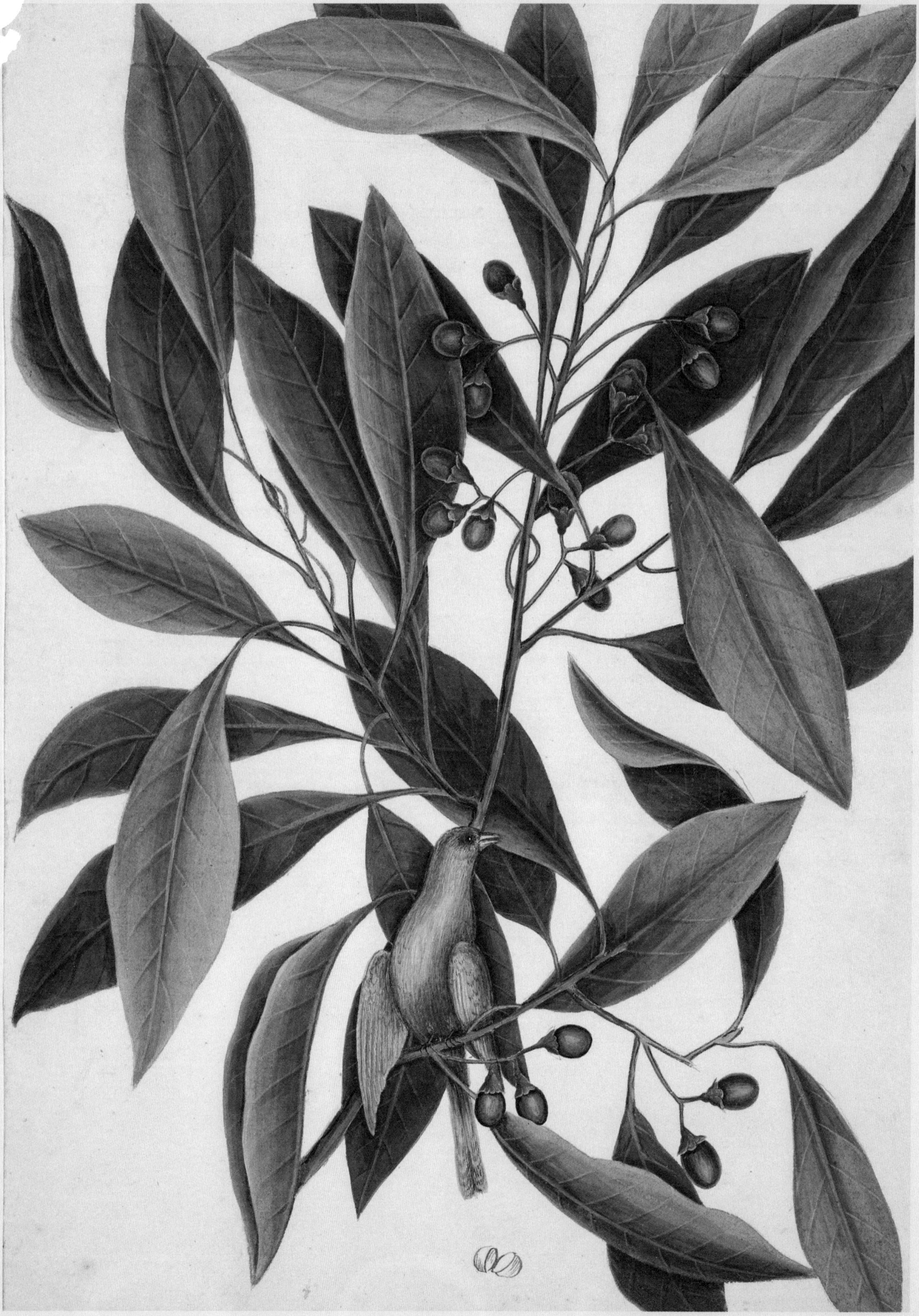

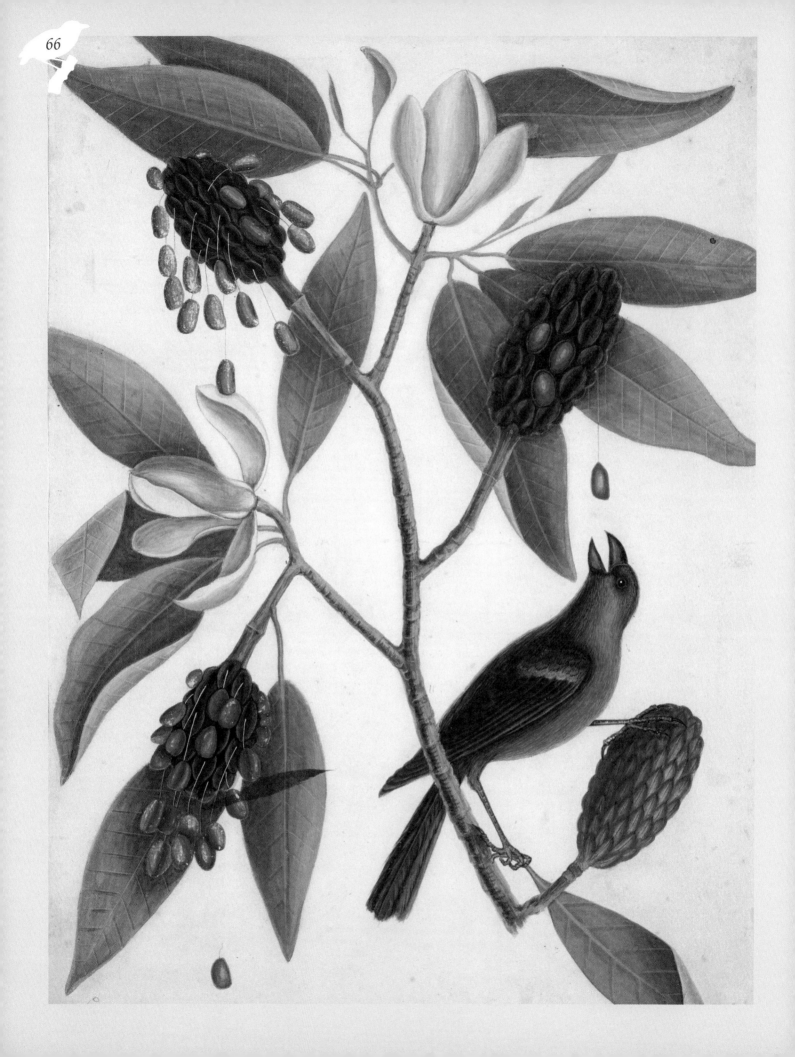

Coccothraustes rubra

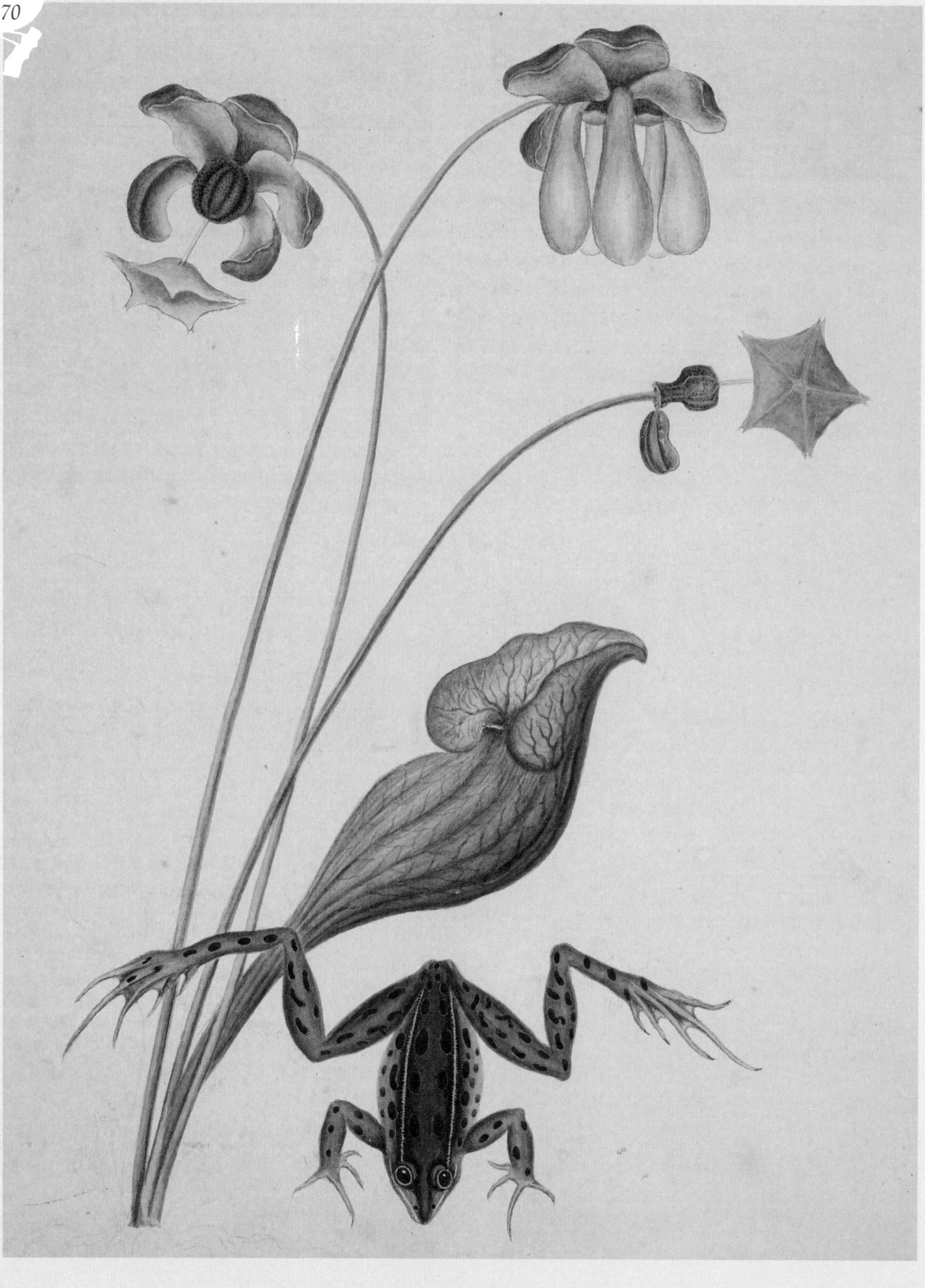

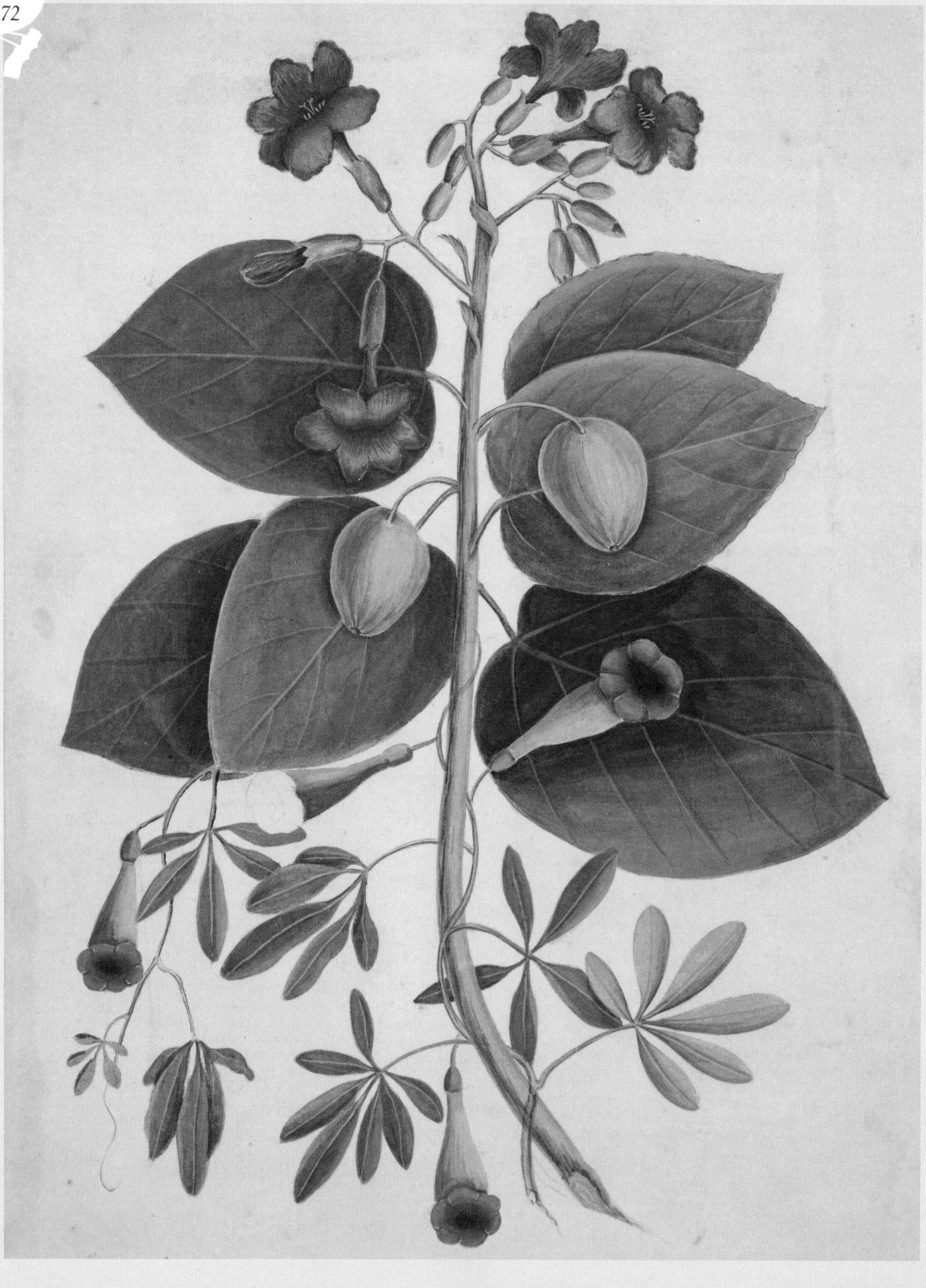

pseudo phalangium ramosum

Bignonia arbor pentaphylla, flore roseo majore, siliquis planis. plum: Cat:

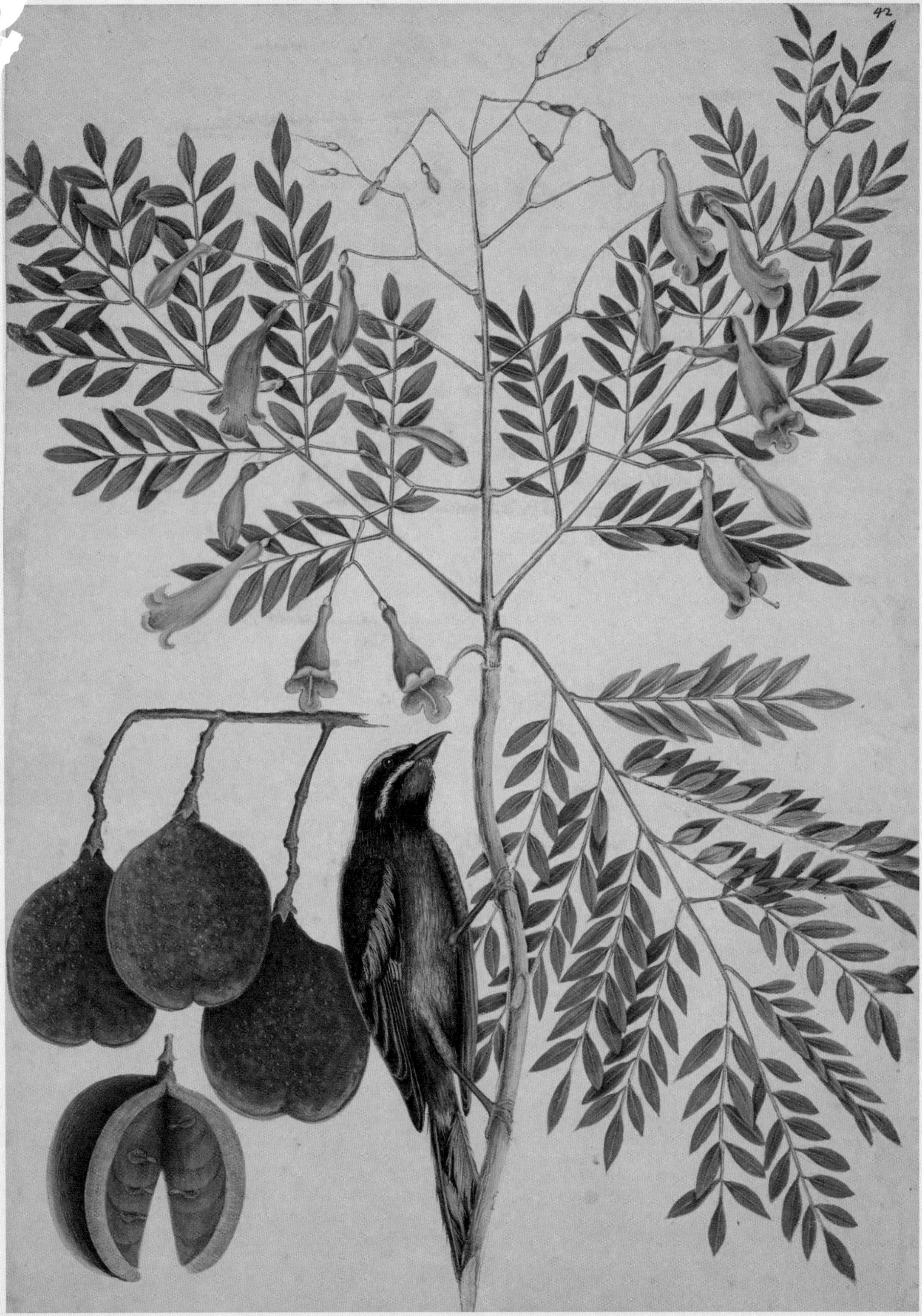
42

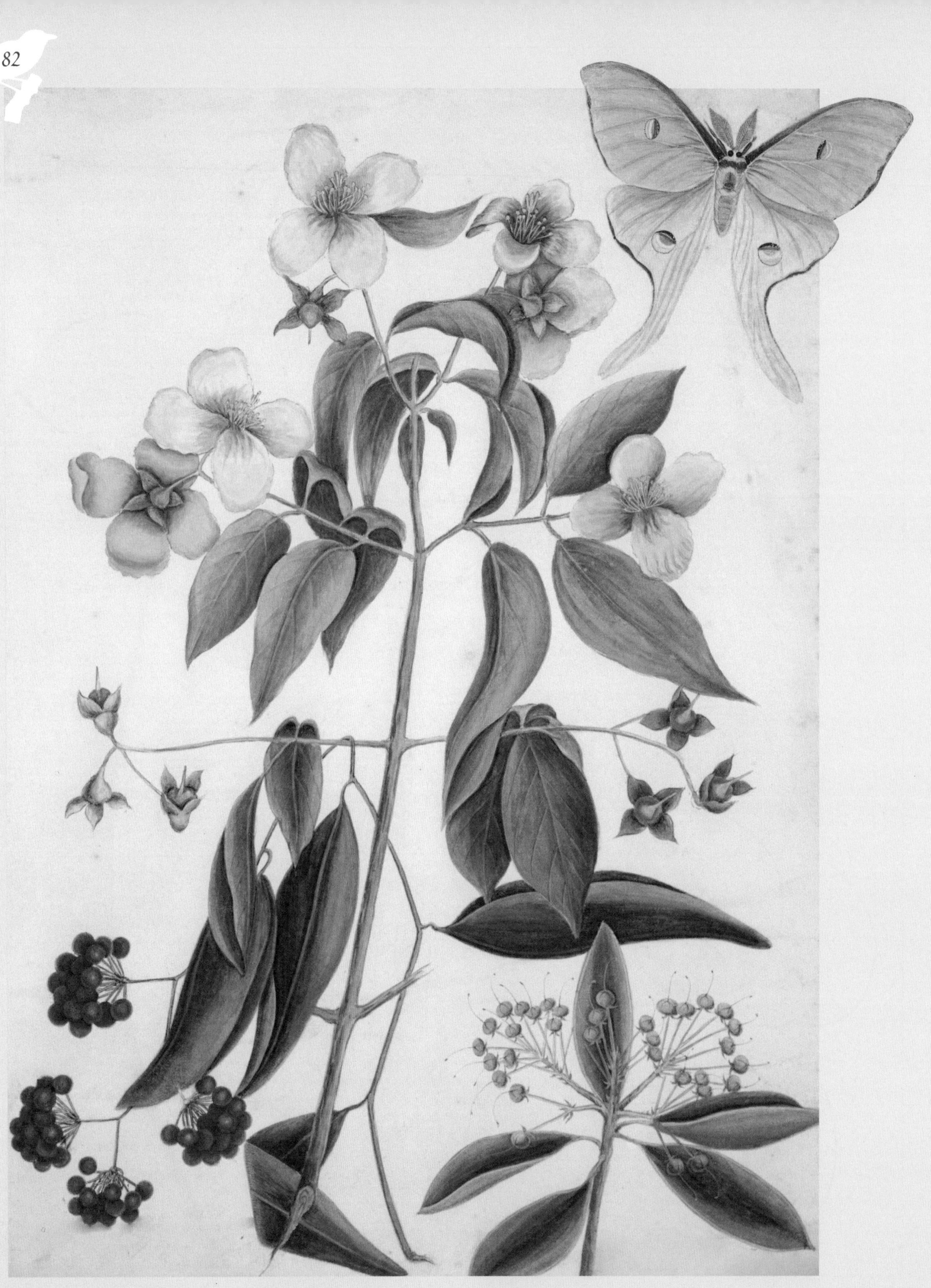

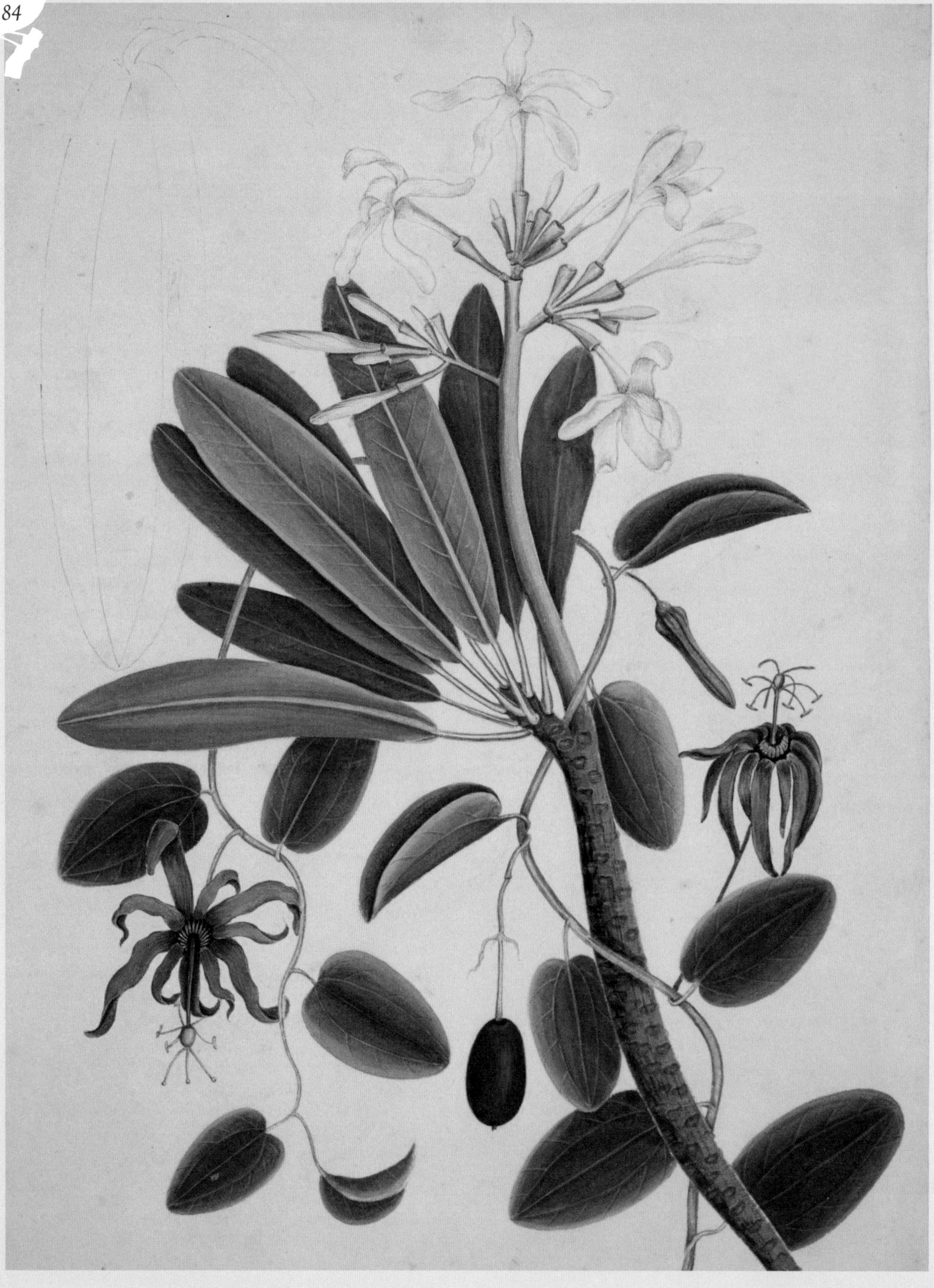

Viscum Caryophilloides Lilij
albi folijs floris labello brevi
purpuree ceteris ex luteo viri-
centibus.

Viscum radice bulbosa
floris labello candi, ceteris
dorsalibe luteis.

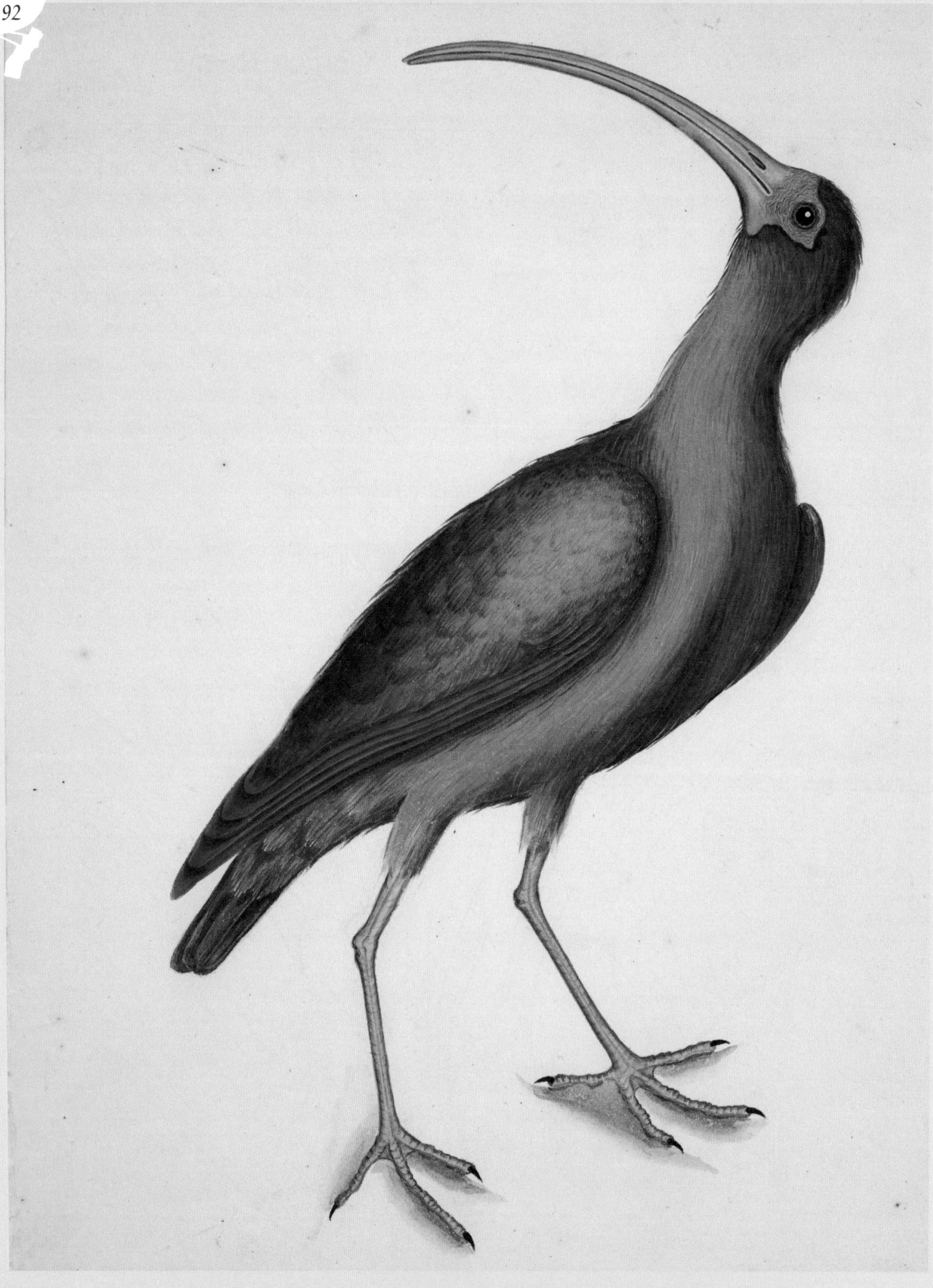